THE WRITING ON THE WALL

First published in Great Britain in 1983
by Methuen Children's Books Ltd.

Printed in Great Britain.
First U.S. Edition
1 2 3 4 5 6 7 8 9 10

Library of Congress Cataloging in Publication D

Garfield, Leon.
    The writing on the wall.

    Summary: Samuel, a kitchen-boy in Babylon, serv
Belshazzar, the King, and his guests at the feast
during which God delivers a message to Belshazzar whi
is interpreted by Judge Daniel.
    1. Daniel, the Prophet—Juvenile literature.
2. Belshazzar—Juvenile literature. 3. Bible stories,
English—O. T. Daniel. [1. Daniel, the Prophet.
2. Belshazzar. 3. Bible stories—O. T.] I. Bragg,
Michael. II. Title.
BS580.D2G37   1983   224′.509505   82-24938
ISBN 0-688-02112-3

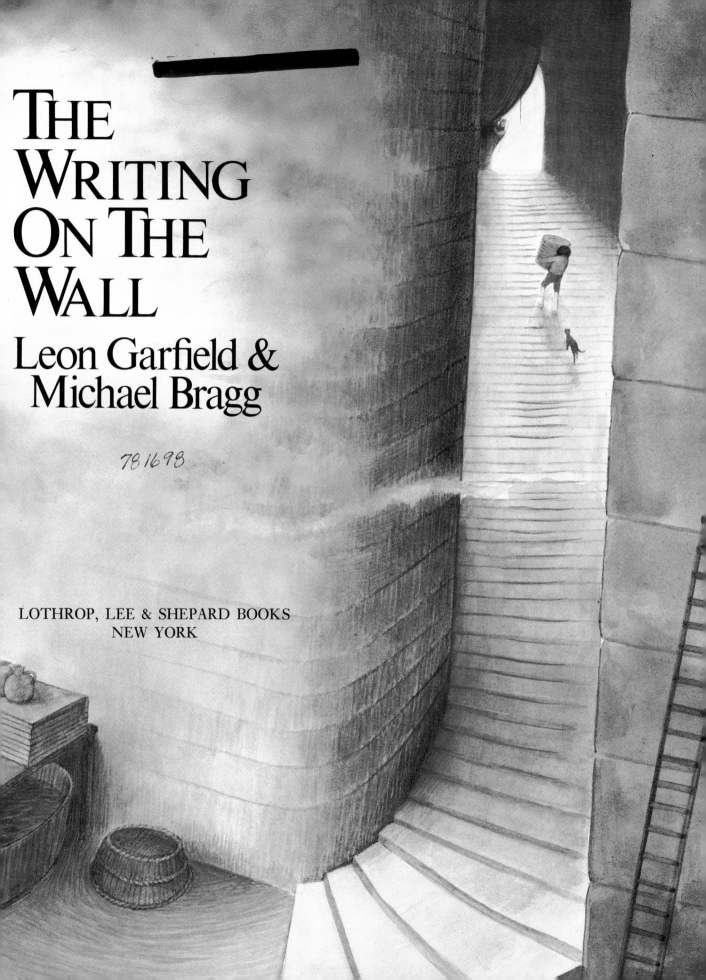

THE WRITING ON THE WALL

Leon Garfield &
Michael Bragg

781698

LOTHROP, LEE & SHEPARD BOOKS
NEW YORK

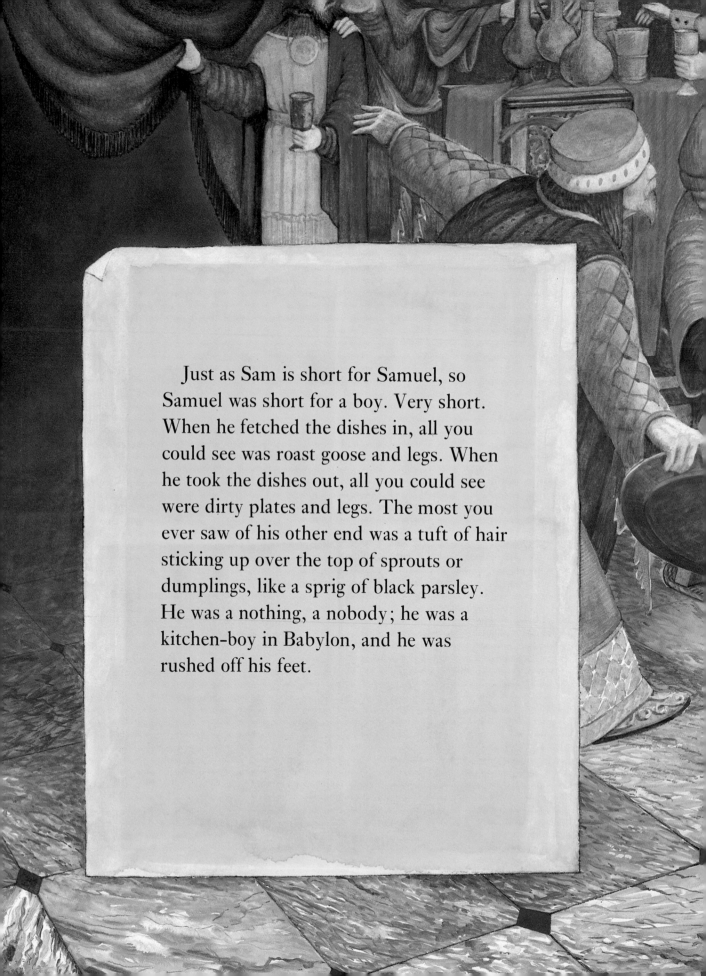

Just as Sam is short for Samuel, so Samuel was short for a boy. Very short. When he fetched the dishes in, all you could see was roast goose and legs. When he took the dishes out, all you could see were dirty plates and legs. The most you ever saw of his other end was a tuft of hair sticking up over the top of sprouts or dumplings, like a sprig of black parsley. He was a nothing, a nobody; he was a kitchen-boy in Babylon, and he was rushed off his feet.

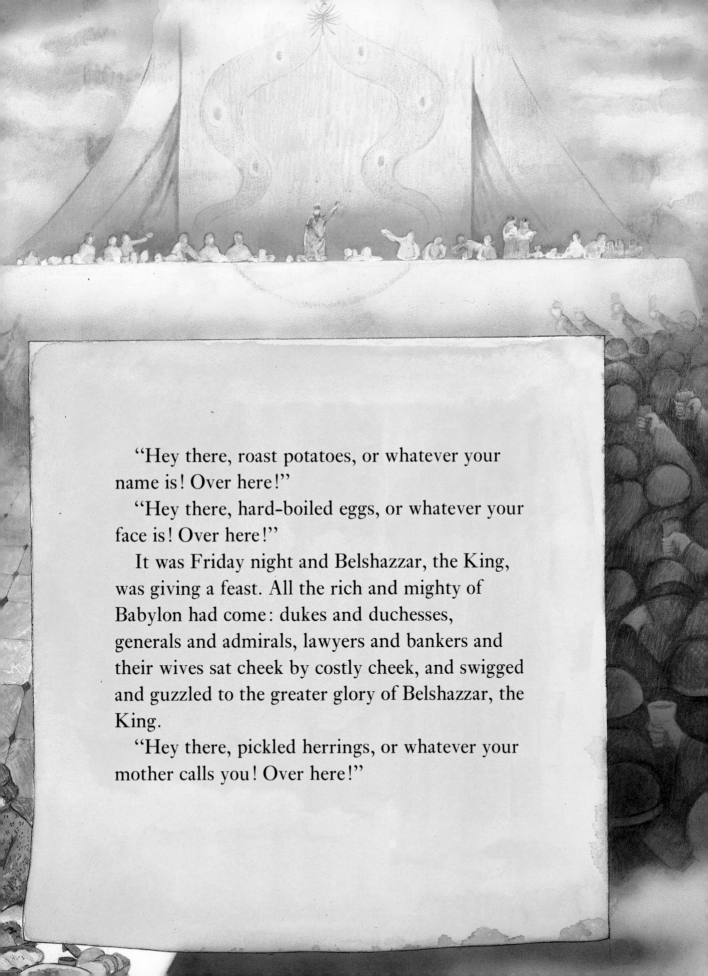

"Hey there, roast potatoes, or whatever your name is! Over here!"

"Hey there, hard-boiled eggs, or whatever your face is! Over here!"

It was Friday night and Belshazzar, the King, was giving a feast. All the rich and mighty of Babylon had come: dukes and duchesses, generals and admirals, lawyers and bankers and their wives sat cheek by costly cheek, and swigged and guzzled to the greater glory of Belshazzar, the King.

"Hey there, pickled herrings, or whatever your mother calls you! Over here!"

Even the gods of Babylon had been summoned to attend. They arrived in carts and on the tops of wagons: ugly great idols covered all over with pearls and rubies, like high-class measles.

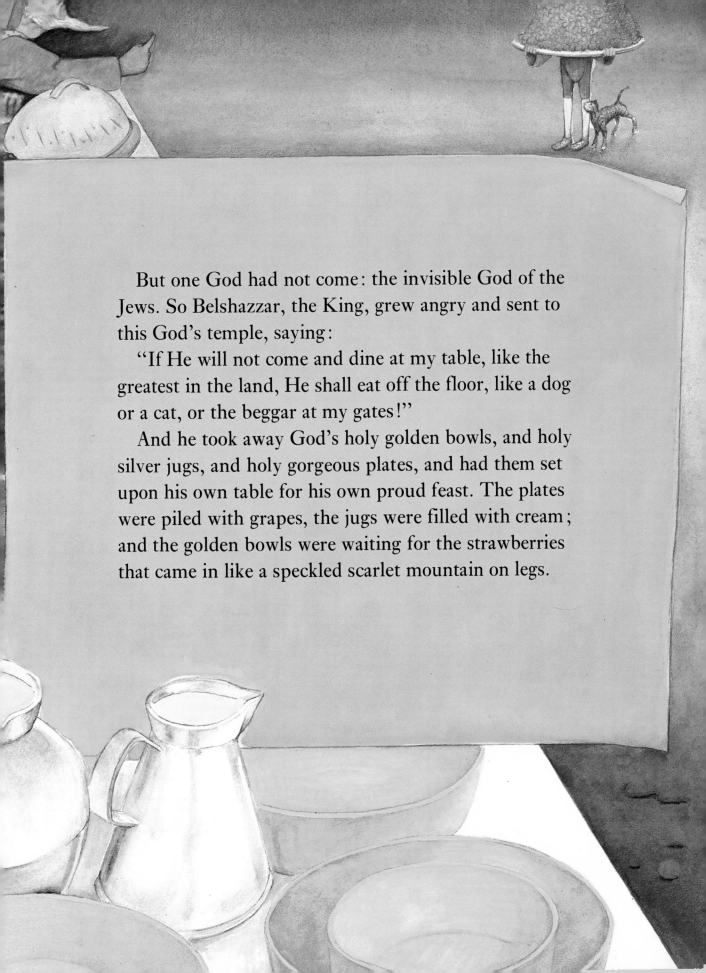

But one God had not come: the invisible God of the Jews. So Belshazzar, the King, grew angry and sent to this God's temple, saying:

"If He will not come and dine at my table, like the greatest in the land, He shall eat off the floor, like a dog or a cat, or the beggar at my gates!"

And he took away God's holy golden bowls, and holy silver jugs, and holy gorgeous plates, and had them set upon his own table for his own proud feast. The plates were piled with grapes, the jugs were filled with cream; and the golden bowls were waiting for the strawberries that came in like a speckled scarlet mountain on legs.

"Hey there, strawberries, or whatever it is those skinny stumps belong to! Over here!"

Samuel stepped, dainty as a bride around a puddle. This wasn't because he was frightened of falling; it was because he didn't want to tread on Mordecai. Mordecai was a cat, a tattered, one-eared, smelly fleabag of a hungry cat. Wherever Samuel went, Mordecai went too, waving his tail and weaving between Samuel's feet like a drift of tabby smoke, with eyes.

Although Mordecai could see what nobody else could see, which was that Samuel had a face, which kept peering down at him around the edge of a dish like the moon in its second quarter, he miaowed at him like everybody else:

"Hey there, fried sprats! Down here!"

Mordecai was starving. There was hardly anything left of him. His sides were almost meeting in the middle; and he was sure that, if he was weighed in the balances, he wouldn't have tipped the scales at a pennyweight.

"Hey there, boiled halibut! Down here! PLEASE!"
Samuel's heart ached for Mordecai; but he was
rushed off his feet by the rich and mighty of Babylon,
and there just wasn't any time for a cat.

"Behold!" cried Belshazzar, the King, as he spooned
up strawberries as bright as blood, and poured on
cream as thick as pride. "What will this God do for His
supper now that Belshazzar has His jugs and bowls?"

He laughed; and all the rich and mighty laughed too.
They shook and swayed and clinked and jingled, like a
miser in a gale.

"This God," he shouted, "will have to come like a
beggar to the hall of Belshazzar, the King!"

He began to laugh again. Then he stopped. His mouth fell open, and a strawberry fell out, and made a bloodstain on the cloth. His eyes bulged, his knees knocked, and he clutched at the table for support.

What was wrong? What was the great King staring at, high up on the wall? The dukes and generals and lawyers and bankers and their wives turned in their seats and looked up at the wall.

"A – A – A – AH!"

Painted faces turned as white as plaster; forks and spoons dropped from trembling fingers and glasses fell and smashed upon the floor.

"HOO – OO – OO – OOH!"

Out of nothing, out of nowhere, a hand had come! It was a hand as pale as death! There was no wrist, no sleeve, no arm. It was just a hand, with fingers that moved along the wall!

Scratch – scratch – scratch! It began to write. Scratch – scratch – scratch! Strange words appeared, words that none could read. Then the hand stopped. It turned and seemed to point at every heart; then it faded into air!

Belshazzar, the King, and all the rich company sat and glared at the writing on the wall, like a feast in stone.

The hall was as quiet as Sunday; and Samuel looked for Mordecai, the cat.

"Pussycat, pussycat, where have you been?" whispered Samuel, as Mordecai came and looked up at him with eyes like empty saucers.

"Under the table," miaowed Mordecai, making a hoop of his back and a crook with his tail, "under the table to look for some cream."

"Pussycat, pussycat, did you find any there?" whispered Samuel.

"Nothing but feet," miaowed Mordecai, "nothing but feet and the legs of a chair."

Samuel listened. Nobody called for him. He waited. Nobody wanted him. He peered around one side of the speckled mountain of strawberries. Nobody was looking at him. He peered around the other side. Everybody was looking at the wall. He didn't know why. All Samuel could see were strawberries and cream . . . and Mordecai, the cat.

Everybody was looking at the wall; except Samuel,
who was watching everybody to make sure they
weren't watching him; and Mordecai the cat, who was
watching Samuel.

"Hey there, you with the face! Cream, down here."

"Hey there, Mordecai! It's time for a cat!"

He lowered his dish, filled up a holy golden bowl
from a holy silver jug, and put it on the floor under the
table of Belshazzar, the King. Then he picked up his
dish, and stood, stock-still, behind the mountain of
strawberries, while tattered, one-eared, smelly old
Mordecai finished off the cream and polished God's
golden bowl with his rough pink tongue.

And all the while, Belshazzar, the King, and the rich
and mighty of Babylon shook and trembled, and stared
at the writing on the wall.

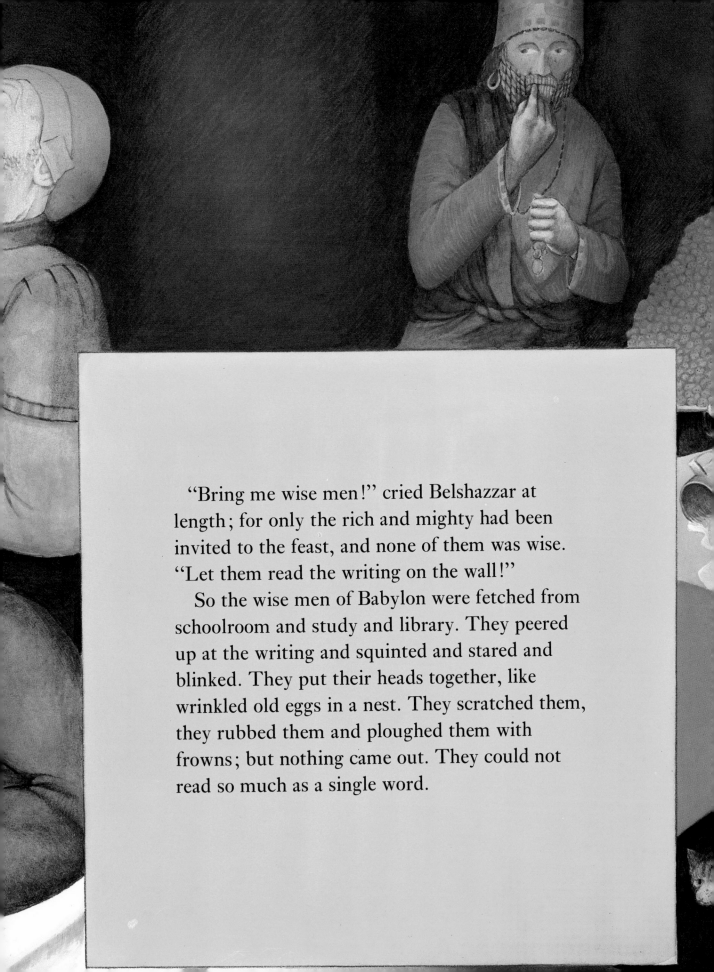

"Bring me wise men!" cried Belshazzar at
length; for only the rich and mighty had been
invited to the feast, and none of them was wise.
"Let them read the writing on the wall!"

So the wise men of Babylon were fetched from
schoolroom and study and library. They peered
up at the writing and squinted and stared and
blinked. They put their heads together, like
wrinkled old eggs in a nest. They scratched them,
they rubbed them and ploughed them with
frowns; but nothing came out. They could not
read so much as a single word.

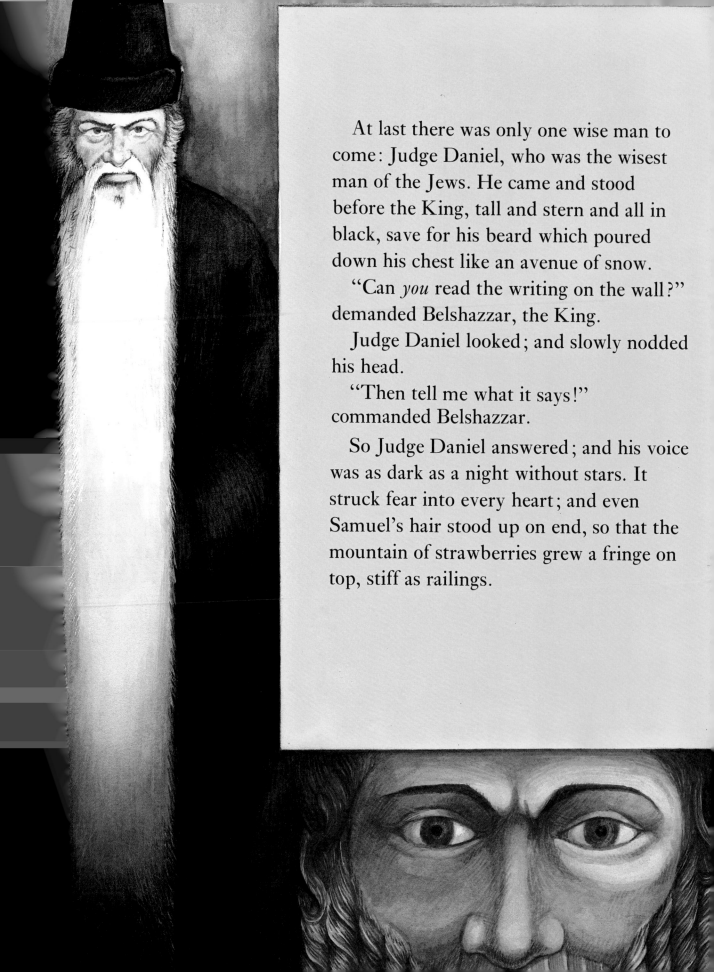

At last there was only one wise man to come: Judge Daniel, who was the wisest man of the Jews. He came and stood before the King, tall and stern and all in black, save for his beard which poured down his chest like an avenue of snow.

"Can *you* read the writing on the wall?" demanded Belshazzar, the King.

Judge Daniel looked; and slowly nodded his head.

"Then tell me what it says!" commanded Belshazzar.

So Judge Daniel answered; and his voice was as dark as a night without stars. It struck fear into every heart; and even Samuel's hair stood up on end, so that the mountain of strawberries grew a fringe on top, stiff as railings.

"Your days are numbered, Belshazzar, the King," said Judge Daniel. "You have been weighed in the balances and found wanting. You have sinned. You have taken from God His silver jugs and golden bowls and set yourself above Him. Therefore your kingdom is finished, Belshazzar, the King. God has finished it."

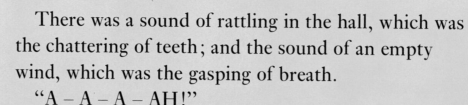

There was a sound of rattling in the hall, which was the chattering of teeth; and the sound of an empty wind, which was the gasping of breath.

"A – A – A – AH!"

Their rich robes grew huge and heavy on the feasters; and their jewelled crowns and coronets seemed like iron fists pressing down on their heads. With shaking limbs and frightened faces they crept away into the night, and hid themselves in shadows and holes in the ground, where they hoped that God would never find them. The strawberry mountain sank out of sight, and under the table of Belshazzar, the King.

At last the hall was empty of all save Judge Daniel in his long black gown and his tall black hat. He gazed at the tumbled chairs, and the broken glasses and the scattered plates; and then at the table of Belshazzar, the King.

"Hey there!" he cried, spying something unusual. "Boy's feet and cat's tail or whatever you are! Over here!"

Samuel came forth; and with him came Mordecai the cat.

"Well?" said Judge Daniel, solemn as a coffin with folded arms. "Who are you?"

"Just another sinner," said Samuel, sorely afraid. "Name of Samuel; and this is Mordecai the cat."

"Is that so?" said Judge Daniel, kneeling down to be on a level so that his beard made a kind of toboggan run ending up in a drift; for Samuel was short for a boy.

"Look," said Samuel, sad as rain on a holiday, "look what I did." And he fetched out from under the table, a holy silver jug and a holy golden bowl. "I took what was God's, and used it for Mordecai, the cat."

Judge Daniel frowned and stroked his beard, and absent-mindedly poured out more cream for Mordecai, the cat.

"Weighed in the balances and found wanting," said Samuel, gazing up at the mysterious writing on the wall. "That's us all right. The pair of us put together wouldn't tip the scales on a pennyweight! Light as dust!"

Judge Daniel sighed and shook his head. "Since when," he asked, tickling the only ear of Mordecai, the cat, "can a kitchen-boy read what all the wise men could not understand? It says on the wall, as plain as anything, that Samuel and Mordecai have been weighed in the balances and found NEEDING." He sighed again. "So go home, Samuel, go home to bed. And take this golden bowl and this silver jug to remind you always."

"To remind me of what?" asked Samuel.

"That God punishes greed, not need," said Judge Daniel, in a voice as soft as dreams.

So Samuel went; and winding between his legs, like a drift of tabby smoke, went Mordecai the cat.